THE ORIGIN OF THE UNIVERSE:
AN EXAMINATION OF THE BIG-BANG
AND STEADY-STATE COSMOGONIES

by

HAROLD S. SLUSHER

ICR Technical Monograph No. 8

INSTITUTE FOR CREATION RESEARCH
San Diego, California 92116

ISBN - 0 - 932766-00-5

Library of Congress Card Catalog Number 78-70532

Copyright 1978

INSTITUTE FOR CREATION RESEARCH

San Diego, California 92116

TABLE OF CONTENTS

THE ORIGIN OF THE UNIVERSE: AN EXAMINATION OF THE BIG-BANG AND STEADY-STATE COSMOGONIES

I. INTRODUCTION

A. COSMOGONIC CONCEPTS

There are two very distinct ways of looking at the origin and history of the universe: creationist and evolutionist. They cannot both be right since they are contradictory.

The evolutionist position holds to a materialistic explanation that says the origin of the universe can be explained completely on the basis of what we observe and study around us at present by just extrapolating this back in time. This position maintains that there operate self-transforming processes in this system of matter and energy (the universe) that changed it from the highly disordered, chaotic state it was in the beginning in their scheme to the very complicated, highly ordered cosmos we observe today. In this scheme, changes occur so slowly that huge quantities of time are necessary for this progression to take place. This naturalistic position says that the universe is all there is; that it is self-contained; that matter and energy arose spontaneously from nothing or they have always existed; and that the physical and chemical laws are "just here."

On the other hand, the creationist position claims that the universe was created by God, an Agent external to this system of matter and energy which He created. Not only were the matter and energy of the universe created, but the highly ordered and complex celestial bodies such as stars, star clusters, galaxies, galaxy clusters, etc. that compose this universe were made by this Being. Ordered arrangements and life itself came from the working of this supernatural Agent. The universe thus began in a highly ordered state with a low entropy and has since begun to run down and deteriorate and lose form and body. This position may involve a short time scale.

These two positions are obviously diametrically opposed. In examining the universe we must look at the data and the basic physical and chemical laws to see which of these models is the stronger so far as being in accord with those laws and the predicting of certain characteristics of this universe. Certainly, at the very least, a hypothesis should be consistent with the observed universe and with the known laws of the creation. There is more to be required, however. The inaccessible past must to some extent conform to the pattern of the present behavior of the universe. Just because the past is inaccessible does not mean it is granted a freedom in which anything can happen. It seems that the evolutionist has "cooked up" a topsy-turvy, Alice-in-Wonderland universe in which anything goes.

B. EVOLUTION DEFINED

Evolution has been defined in a manner that makes it rather obvious what it actually involves. The evolutionist considers evolution to be a one-way process that is irreversible in time; producing newness and variety as well as leading to higher degrees of organization and complexity and differentiation, yet more integrated. He would say that it is a process of self-transformation. Evolutionist astronomers in the main, propose as the explanation of the universe an explosion to form a state of chaos (the "big bang"). The evolutionary processes then begin to act supposedly bringing about a progression from disorder to order, or from chaos to a highly ordered, complex universe. Chaos and cosmos are represented as the initial and present status of the universe, respectively. This "big bang" explosion is surely the opposite to any explosions we see occurring today and any that man is able to produce since they destroy order and body.

The process of nuclear synthesis, the origin of the nuclei that comprise the atoms, further represents a progression from disorder to order. The doctrine of organic evolution postulates the movement from life in the simplest forms to the present highly complex, differentiated, and integrated world. This is again disorder-to-order progression; simple to complex, all said to occur spontaneously.

The evolutionists have also advanced the concept of so-called "prebiological evolution" which is an idea based on spontaneous advancement from the simple to the complex. Supposedly things start from simple chemicals like ammonia, methane, hydrogen and water to the fantastically complicated giant molecules such as life's templates RNA and DNA. Life supposedly "exploded" into being after an alleged billion of years of evolution of the template molecules. It would seem then that organic evolution is truly a doctrine of spontaneous generation. It is a self-transforming process requiring the "magic" of infinite time in order to make the cosmos in spite of moving in the face of continual violation of the Second Law of Thermodynamics.

C. THE SECOND LAW OF THERMODYNAMICS

This concept of disorder to order, chaos to cosmos (the evolutionary claim) is directly contradicted by the very basic and underlying principle of physics called the Second Law of Thermodynamics.

Thermal energy is disordered energy. The amount of energy of a system is measured by the state function U and the amount of disorder by a state function S called the entropy. In any process that occurs in nature, the total entropy increases. The principle of entropy increase (a corollary of the Second Law of Thermodynamics) is one of the most profound laws of physics. Its ramifications extend throughout chemistry and biology, as well as physics and engineering. The Second Law of Thermodynamics, as formulated by Clausius and Lord Kelvin, has been stated in many different but logically equivalent ways. Clausius stressed the utility of entropy and showed that the Second Law was the same as saying that the total entropy increases in any process. The microscopic interpretation of entropy as a measure of molecular disorder was discovered by Boltzmann.

Many processes that would seem possible according to the First Law of Thermodynamics, because they do conserve energy, in fact never occur. For example, a brick resting on a horizontal road never spontaneously accelerates along the road by gathering up thermal energy from the road. If this process occurred, the energy which is randomly distributed over many molecules of the road would be converted into an ordered motion of the brick as a whole. This transformation from disorder to order is quite compatible with the First Law, but it does not happen.

The reverse process does occur and it illustrates a feature present in all our experience. When a brick is projected along the road, it slows down as the kinetic energy due to the ordered motion of the brick as a whole is transformed into thermal energy associated with disordered molecular motion within the road and the brick.

Examination of this and many other processes reveals that there is a general rule which determines the direction in which energy transformations occur. Ordered energy is transformed into disordered energy; that is, order ⟶ disorder. But the reverse transformation is not observed. The disorder in one object can be reduced in a process only if there is more than compensating increase in the disorder of other objects that participate in the process.

This law which determines the direction in which processes occur can be given a quantitative formulation in terms of entropy. The entropy of an object is a measure of its molecular disorder. Increasing disorder implies increasing entropy. The rule is that processes take place only in the direction that increases the total entropy of the participating objects. In any process, the total entropy of the participating objects is increased. The total entropy never decreases.

Life is a one-way street. We are born, we grow old, and we die. The physical law that distinguishes the past from the future, that puts the arrow on time is the entropy increase. The situation with lower entropy (less disorder) must come before that with higher entropy (more disorder).

Any real process involves an increase in the total entropy. A reversal of such a process, leading to a restoration of the initial entropies of all the participating objects, would therefore involve a decrease in entropy. Entropy-increasing processes are irreversible processes.

The Second Law is relevant not only in engineering and physics but also in chemistry and biology. The direction in which chemical reactions proceed is governed by the principle of entropy increase. In biological processes, if we look at all the objects participating in the process, we find that the obvious entropy decreases have been more than matched by entropy increases elsewhere.

The entropy increases that occur in natural processes measure the increased disorder, a total entropy increase is associated with a lost opportunity to obtain useful mechanical work. When a process leads to an increase in the total entropy, some energy which could have been used to perform macroscopic mechanical work has been degraded to a form in which it is unavailable for work. Natural processes occur in a direction such that, on a scale of unavailability, energy runs downhill.

The entropy-increasing direction of all natural processes tends to bring about uniformity of temperature, pressure, and composition. The "heat death" for the universe is inferred from the law of entropy when a situation of complete uniformity is reached.

Since no process could then increase the total entropy, physical, chemical, and biological changes would cease.

This can be summed up by saying that a one-step creation during which the whole (the universe) was wound up, from which condition it has been running down ever since took place. In the evolutionist scheme there is a continuous violation of the Second Law occurring somewhere in the universe. On the basis of observations and experimental results the first conclusion seems correct. The universe is alleged by the evolutionist to be one big isolated system, and if that is the case, it cannot have moved itself from a chaotic state to the cosmos. In fact, we see today a universe that is losing order, form, and body. The entropy law would seem to demand a supernatural origin of this universe that initially contained much more information or order than it does now. Obviously the evolutionary hypothesis fails to be consistent with the entropy law as seen from George Gamow's statement:

> "We may also assume that in that distant past our universe was considerably less differentiated and complex than it is now and that the state of matter at that time could be accurately described by the classical concept of a 'primordial chaos'...the problem of scientific cosmogony can be formulated as an attempt to reconstruct the evolutionary process which led from simplicity of the early days of creation to the present immense complexity of the universe around us."[1]

D. PHILOSOPHICAL ASPECTS OF COSMOLOGY AND COSMOGONY

Astronomy, when considering cosmology, becomes highly speculative. The arguments pro and con regarding the origin of the universe and its organization, reflect the convictions and biases of those who do the arguing. By argument is meant the reason or reasons offered in proof of a statement or belief. The term cosmology denotes a branch of metaphysics that treats of the character of the universe as an orderly system, or cosmos.

The part of the universe that we can observe is at most only a very small portion of what we have reason to believe exists. Thus, considerations over and above the ordinary scientific process of inductive generalization are introduced and those considerations are philosophical in nature and gives cosmology a philosophical slant. Thus, by definition, cosmology is philosophical in character. The religious convictions, ranging from atheism to Christianity, are bound to color individual cosmological thought. Cosmology necessarily to some extent includes the philosophy of cosmogony, which deals with hypotheses concerning the origin and change of the universe. Today cosmology and cosmogony are used interchangeably.

The cosmologist cannot simply solve backwards in time the equations describing change in the universe, but has to take chosen variants of the initial state and follow through to the confrontation of observations. The snag is that this depends on the prejudices, likes and dislikes of cosmologists.

The approach to cosmology normally follows two distinct ways. The first is the observational approach. We attempt to observe what the universe is "really" like. The other approach is synthetic in which hypothetical models of the universe are constructed and then these models are compared to the observations to find the degree of fit. This second approach might seem to be superfluous. However, observations are not all that are needed. Since only a limited portion of the universe is accessible to observation, cosmological theories can never be verified directly.

Any observation has to be interpreted and can only be interpreted within the framework of some concept, even if that concept is just common sense. Common sense implies a model. It is three-dimensional; time measurements can be completely divorced from distance measurements; bodies obey the Newtonian laws of motion; there are laws of conservation and of momentum.

It would be of value to consider some of the dilemmas and assumptions of cosmology:

1.   Dilemmas in Cosmology

A dilemma is an argument presenting an antagonist with two or more alternatives, each equally conclusive against him.   The cosmologist is faced with a number of dilemmas, some of which are enumerated below.

a.   Our instantaneous snapshot view of the universe gives us a certain picture. But what, we may ask, was the snapshot view a distant yesterday?   And what will be the instantaneous picture a distant tomorrow?   The cosmologist attempts to sift the evidence available in today's view, and from that construct the past and predict the future on the basis of the universe as he can see it at this instant.   So far as reconstructing the past, the entropy law says this cannot be done except to say that the universe was much more complicated and highly organized in bygone times than now.

b.   A further complication involves the time lag for arrival of information from celestial events.   Except for information provided by all our senses, excluding light, information that is transferred to and from us rides along on a beam of electromagnetic radiation (light, radiant heat, or radio waves).   There exists a lag between the occurrence of an event and the arrival of an electromagnetic signal about it, of one millisecond for every 300 km distance, assuming light travels at a constant speed in a vacuum and along straight lines.   Astronomical occurrences are thus immersed in a complication provided by the travel time of light waves over a variety of cosmic distances.   In our instantaneous snapshot we are comparing information about the space position, the luminosity, the motion, and the physical properties of celestial objects that may have taken quite a while to get here.

c.   Even if the cosmologist were to be able to accommodate the complications of the time element into his viewpoint, there are more serious problems plaguing his efforts. Suppose that all galaxies were intrinsically the same brightness (not likely, though, but useful in illustrating a basic aspect of the appearance of the universe). From the inverse square law we can infer the relative distances to all galaxies. If the distribution of galaxies is homogeneous, then doubling the distance should increase the galaxy count eightfold; tripling it should produce a galaxy count 27 times as large. Actual counts of galaxies show a rate substantially less than this. If allowed to stand without correction, this feature of the galaxy counts implies a thinning out with distance in all directions, and that we are at the very center of the highest concentration of matter in the universe. Also, the velocity of recession of galaxies appears to increase with distance in every direction. This would argue that we are at the original center of the universe.

With respect to the light emitted, the rapid recession of a galaxy, say, results in the dimming of the light from an energy effect and an attenuation effect. According to the Doppler principle, light waves are stretched out because of the recessional motion; the initial and final positions of a wave leave from different points. Longer wave length means lower frequency; lower frequency implies less energetic photons. The attentuation means that fewer photons will arrive at the photographic plate each second. Both these effects contribute to the need for longer exposures than would otherwise be necessary. In other words, the photographic record shows galaxies to be dimmer than they would be if they were at rest.

When galaxy counts are adjusted for these dimming effects, it appears that the number of galaxies per unit volume of space increases with distance. From this we still appear to be at the center of the universe, but now it coincides with the point of least concentration of matter. The fact that we appear to be at the center is very bothersome to most cosmologists since it's distinctly distasteful to them that man might have a special place in time and/or in space in the universe. Further, this is particularly bothersome to evolutionary cosmologists since the above evidence points to galaxies all the same age and the nearby galaxies are obviously young galaxies.

d. Another difficulty involves the observed increase in magnitude of the red shift with distance. Taken on face value it would seem that the velocity of recession increases as galaxies reach ever greater distances. This would lead to an accelerating universe. The principle effect of acceleration is to shorten the time span required between the origin and the presently observed state of the universe. This time scale leads to a value for the age of the universe less than the value the evolutionists put on the age of our own galaxy.

No

This is not true

e. There are further problems which strongly establish the philosophical nature of cosmology such as the attempt to decide whether the physical laws are laws of the universe or universal laws; the establishment of the uniqueness of the universe and the nature of this uniqueness--essential or accidental; the problem of decisions regarding the stability of equilibrium of the universe.

f. If the universe is expanding and the galaxies are moving away from us, how do we explain those few galaxies with spectra that are blue-shifted since this would indicate approach rather than recession? *No problem!*

2. Some Cosmological Assumptions

There are quite a number of basic assumptions made regarding the universe, particularly by those proposing naturalistic explanations for the universe. It would be profitable for us to discuss some of these assumptions. Most naturalistic cosmologies include the concept of the expanding universe and one or both of the so-called cosmological assumptions. These need to be discussed thoroughly.

      a. The Cosmological Assumption states that the universe looks the same (when a sufficient volume of space is viewed) from any location in the universe. Models are called isotropic which accept the Cosmological Assumption (technically, they are homogeneous, having the same density throughout, and isotropic, having the same physical properties in every direction). There is no real scientific evidence for this assumption. *yes there is!!* This reminds one of when philosophers insisted that the motions of the planets must be circular and uniform because of an irrelevant aesthetic concept of "perfection." *There is too!*

Herbert Dingle has pointed out that the Cosmological Assumption "transferred to the universe the wider characteristics which relativity had found to belong to coordinate systems. Because coordinate systems, being pure fictions, were all precisely equivalent so far as objective validity was concerned, the cosmological presumption declared that all aspects of the universe must be precisely equivalent also. It is like saying that because all languages are equally valid for stating the propositions of Euclid, therefore, all propositions of Euclid must be equivalent to one another."[2] The Cosmological Assumption in the light of actual evidence does not seem to be correct. The observations appear to indicate a hierarchical universe that consists of a hierarchy of objects: galaxies, clusters of galaxies, clusters of clusters of galaxies, etc., up to the size of the universe. Each higher-order cluster is bigger, consisting of a group of the next lower-order clusters, but it has a lower density of matter than its constituent clusters. The Cosmological Assumption is denied because the universe looks different when viewed from inside a galaxy than it does when seen from outside a super cluster.   Gerard de Vaucouleurs[3] argues convincingly that a hierarchical cosmology seems to fit the observations since they indicate that galaxies form clusters, and these clusters form bigger clusters, etc.   The observations show a continuing decrease in density with increase in size for clusters up to the largest clustering known.

b.   Another outright assumption held particularly by the adherents to the steady-state hypothesis is the Perfect Cosmological Principle, or as Herbert Dingle calls it, the Cosmological Presumption. The Cosmological Presumption states that the universe looks the same at any time, as well as from any location.   For this Cosmological Presumption there is no evidence of any kind at all.   The Cosmological Presumption is obviously an idea conforming to the tastes of the investigator and not expressing any regularities found in experience.

c.   The naturalistic models described in this monograph are based on general relativity, which does not rest on any sort of experimental basis.   The solar system tests of general relativity have not been successful thus far.

d.   It would seem that modern cosmology is very similar to medieval scholasticism.   As de Vaucouleurs put it: "Often the borderline between sophistication and sophistry, between numeration and numerology seems very precarious indeed."[4]   There seems a serious loss of contact with empirical evidence and observational facts.   Some cosmogonists refuse to accept results when they are in conflict with their intellectually appealing views of the universe.   They seem to live in a fictitious or nonexistent universe rather than the actual world.

II.   OBSERVATIONS TO EXPLAIN

A.   INTRODUCTION

Virtually all modern cosmology is based on two phenomena: one is that the night sky is dark; the other is known as the "red shift," interpretations of which have led to some of today's popular distance scales in the universe.

The red shift is probably the single most important observational fact on which modern cosmology is based. Consequently, the shift has received a great deal of attention, and the controversies that have sprung up regarding its interpretation remain unsettled at present.

B. THE RED SHIFT

The observational fact is that in general, the larger the apparent magnitude number of a galaxy, the more its spectral lines are displaced toward the longer wavelength region of the spectrum, compared to a laboratory source of these spectral lines. Thus the fainter the galaxy, the redder it becomes. It should be recognized also that the red shift is a statistical effect. The statistics from which the functional form of the variation is found are constantly being re-examined. Also, it is not quite clear that no dispersion occurs, or, in other words, that the red shift does not depend on the wave-lengths of the light. If dispersion does occur, many present interpretations will have to be revised.

Many interpretations of the red shift other than the classical Doppler effect have been proposed:

1. One possibility is that the galaxies are at relative rest, but their light has become "tired" during its journey through space, so that the wavelength is increased and, thus, has been lost. Among the energy-degradation mechanisms that have been mentioned in this connection are possible photon-neutrino interactions and photon-photon interactions. Neither has ever been observed in the laboratory. Presumably, however, many such scatterings could occur over vast distance.

It is by no means obvious what the cross sections for such reactions might be. It is doubtful that we could even see remote galaxies at all, much less the occurrence of dispersionless energy loss, should light interact with neutrinos of various energies.   Alternatively, if photon-photon scattering is responsible for the red shift, one might expect to observe striking effects in eclipsing binary stars.   These are not observed.

2.   Another possibility is that the red shift is gravitational in origin.   Some experiments have been interpreted to indicate that gravitational effects of masses can redshift light; in this interpretation it is believed that light has to do work in escaping from a gravitational "well" such as a star and is therefore reddened.   It is thought that experimental confirmation of the gravitational red shift has been provided by a Mossbauer measurement of the energy of gamma ray photons that are emitted and travel vertically upward through a distance of about 30 meters on the earth's surface in which they must expend work against a planetary gravitational field.   The energy of each such photon is found to be minutely less at the upper detector than it was at the source below.   If the cosmological red shift were to have a gravitational origin it would lead to the notion that one galaxy lies in a gravitational "hole" in the universe. Actually, the gravitational redshift is a geometrical explanation in terms of the curved geometry of general relativity and consequently lacking in proof.

3.   A radical view differing from the conventional hypotheses has been proposed by Pecker, Roberts and Vigier[5] for an explanation of some red shifts by means of mutual interactions between photons. This view proposes that light particles have a rest mass not exactly zero ($<10^{-48}$g), and are capable of speeds less than the fundamental speed predicted by the hypothesis of special relativity.

The proposed explanation is that by mutual interaction between photons, a photon traveling through a "cloud"of other photons could lose energy and, thus, be reddened.

This interaction explains what are referred to as anomalous galactic red shifts as being the simple result of variations of temperature between one galaxy and another which affect the density of the photon cloud associated with those galaxies. The photons on their way out collide inelastically with other photons of the radiation field or cloud of photons near the surface of the source, and the cumulative effect of these collisions is to redden the photons coming out. The three theorists derived an equation whereby the density of the photon cloud and thus the red shift of photons going through depends on the temperature of the source. Occasionally, two apparently normal galaxies appear physically connected and yet have different red shifts. In this hypothesis the anomalous red shift differences between two galaxies that are obviously so very close to each other would be due to a difference in their internal temperatures. Similarly the hypothesis can explain a discrepancy in the red shift at the edge of the sun.

The proposal has several other consequences. It can explain a troublesome anomaly in the distribution of pulsating stars within our galaxy. In electrodynamics it would mean that photons do not move at what is believed by the relatavists to be the universal limiting speed (the "speed of light"). It would explode modern cosmology by explaining the red shifts of the most distant objects, the alleged evidence for the expanding universe and the rest of modern cosmology, as the result of scattering of their light by the universal background radiation, the so-called three-degree blackbody radiation.

Pecker, Roberts and Vigier propose an experimental test of their hypothesis in which a gamma ray beam and laser pulses would traverse the same horizontal path. If there are inelastic collisions, photons of different frequencies from the original would show up at the end of the path.

4.   In 1973, W. G. Tifft[6] of the Steward Observatory reported that the redshifts

of a group of galaxies in the center of the Coma Cluster separated into three distinct bands when plotted against the galaxies' apparent magnitudes. The bands were significant with a confidence level in excess of 99% according to Tifft. When Tifft plotted the actual positions of his galaxies in relation to the center of the Coma Cluster he found that the galaxies in each of the three groups are uniformly distributed about the cluster's central region. From Tifft's point of view, short of some contrived effect that would assign just the right systematic speed to a galaxy depending on the type of radiation it emits, the Doppler shift interpretation does not appear possible.

C. THE DARK NIGHT SKY (OLBERS' PARADOX)

Suppose that a Euclidean space were uniformly filled with stars. Light emitted by stars in a shell at some distance from an observer would be proportional to the volume of the shell $4\pi r^2 dr$. Of this light, a fraction inversely proportional to the square of the distance of this shell would be incident on the observer's telescope, since light intensity drops as the inverse square of the distance: $L \propto 4\pi r^2 dr \left(\frac{1}{r^2}\right)$. From each spherical shell of certain thickness an observer would therefore receive an amount of light proportional to the thickness of the shell alone: $L \propto 4\pi dr$. On calculating out to infinite distance, we find that the light received by the observer should have infinite brightness: $L_{total} = 4\pi dr$. This infinity arises only because we have not taken into account the self-shadowing of stars. A foreground star will prevent an observer from seeing a star in a more distant shell, provided both stars lie along the same line of sight. When shadowing is taken into account we find that the sky should only be as bright as the surface of a typical star, not infinitely bright. Of course, that still is much brighter than the daytime sky; and the night sky is much fainter still.

To someone who strongly believes in the infinite size and age of the universe, this would appear paradoxical.   Olbers first advanced the argument in 1826.   If we try to circumvent the argument by introducing curved space this will not help.   In such a space the area of a sphere drawn about an observer is of the form $S = 4\ a^2 \Theta^{-2}(\chi)$ and is a function of distance χ alone.   The number of stars in a spherical shell is proportional to $S(\chi)\,d\chi$. But the amount of light reaching the observer from that shell also reduced by a factor $S(\chi)$, and these two factors cancel to give the same distance independence obtained for flat space.

It could be argued that interstellar dust might absorb the light.   But in an infinitely old universe, dust would come into radioactive equilibrium with stars and would emit as much light as was absorbed.   The dust would then either emit as brightly as the stars, or else it would evaporate into a gas that either transmitted light or else again emitted as the stars.

As long as galaxies themselves are distributed more or less randomly, this argument for a bright night sky remains valid, and only the overall space density of stars in the universe needs to be taken into account.   That stars aggregate in galaxies, rather than being homogeneously distributed, does not affect the validity of the argument.

Unless we wish to suggest that no laws of physics hold for phenomena on such a scale we are forced into one of three conclusions:

1.   The density or luminosity of stars at large distances diminishes.

2.   The constants of physics vary with time.

3.   There are large systematic motions of stars that give rise to spectral shifts.

Argument 1 would hold if the universe were very young--stars would only have been radiating a short time.

Argument 2 forms the basis of some cosmologies that postulate that such quantities as the gravitational constant might vary from one epoch to the next.   Since these constants affect the rate at which stars emit light, it might be that stars only started shining brightly in recent times. The universe would then not be filled with as much radiation as Olbers calculated.

Argument 3 states that an expanding universe need not be bright since the radiation from distant galaxies is less intense by the time it reaches the observer. As photons reach the observer from points closer to the cosmic horizon, where the red shift of galaxies approach infinity, their energy and arrival rate approaches zero.

This paradox is useful because it places most stringent conditions on cosmological models. A model that is to be taken seriously must assure us that the night sky remains dark.

In the Newtonian cosmology Olbers' paradox might be resolved if a finite universe were assumed and we are situated at the center of it, or if the universe were quite young.

III. THE BIG-BANG COSMOGONIC HYPOTHESIS

A. THE BIG BANG

If the red shifts are truly Doppler shifts, and if the universe is a nonhierarchical system, then it would seem that the universe is expanding (the galaxies are spreading apart), and as it does so, it thins out or matter becomes more tenuous with passing time. Provided no new matter is created to fill the void left by departing galaxies, the total mass of the universe remains constant. It is maintained in this hypothesis that all of the mass of the universe must have originally been together in one location, in the form of a primeval atom composed of subatomic particles and radiation, or even just a blob of energy of extremely high temperature. This would constitute an initial state, the "original" creation. According to the big-bang hypothesis, about 2×10^{10} (20 billion) years ago all of the matter and energy of the universe were concentrated in a single body in which the density was $\approx 10^{25}$ g/cm^3 and the temperature was $\approx 10^{16}$ K° (ten million billion degrees).

For some reason, the primeval atom exploded, sending matter in all directions, with the fastest traveling material being farthest from the center at any given time. Out of this matter condensed all of the cosmic features that we see such as clusters of galaxies, galaxies, clusters of stars, stars, etc. In this nature-myth, those parts of the primeval atom that had the greatest relative speeds are now concentrated in the distant galaxies that are believed to be receding from us with high speeds.

Radio astronomy observations by Arno Penzias and Robert Wilson of the Bell Telephone Laboratories led to the discovery in 1965 of a weak, isotropic continuous background radiation from 0.2 to 21 cm. The wavelength distribution and intensity of this radiation corresponds to the energy spectrum of a blackbody at 3°K.

The existence of such radiation was theoretically predicted by George Gamow. Gamow argued that the expansion of the primeval fireball would result in a decrease in temperature with time. Not all energy would be converted into matter. Most would continue to be thermal in character, degrading ultimately to a temperature of about 3°K in 10 to 20 billion years. It is believed to represent the residual energy of the initial cataclysm called the big bang. However, it should be noted that this background radiation can be explained on a different basis than an explosion or big bang.

B. ARGUMENTS AGAINST THE BIG-BANG HYPOTHESIS

Some of the difficulties inherent in the big-bang hypothesis are the following:

1. It is predicated on a Doppler shift interpretation of the red shift of the galaxies. As already mentioned, some strong objections have been voiced against this interpretation for several reasons. A very important one is that it leads to tremendously

large magnitudes of the velocities of recession. The speeds in some cases approach the speed of light.

Also, the "fact" of galaxies moving apart can be explained by many other states of matter and energy than a primeval atom that exploded. For that matter, the alleged explosion produces radiation and high-speed elementary particles, not galaxies. The galaxies moving apart has nothing whatever to do with the expanding motion of debris from an explosion. But for sake of argument can an expansion be associated with other models?

E. A. Milne and others have proposed models of the universe that will give expansion without explosions, but the latest important discussion along this line is by A. D. Allen[7]. It would be of great worth to examine Allen's arguments somewhat. This discussion follows Allen's paper referred to above.

If either of two different initial states of the universe S_1 or S_2 results in a final state T, the fact that the universe is in the state T cannot be used to conclude that the system was once in state S_1. Nor can it be used to conclude it was in state S_2. It was in either state S_1 or S_2 if they are the only possible initial states, but if there are many initial states leading to state T, then the fact that a system is in state T tells one very little about the initial state of the system. Before continuing this examination we should discuss the Hubble law briefly.

The supposed expansion of the galaxies is believed representable by the Hubble law: $v = H_o r$ where v = speed of the galaxy, r = distance of the galaxy from the observer, and H_o = Hubble's constant. The validity of this expression has been questioned and is challenged seriously by the red shifts of quasars located apparently close to the nuclei of some "nearby" galaxies.

The major problem for putting the Hubble law on any sort of footing is finding the distances to the galaxies for which red shifts are measured. Only for the nearest galaxies can we detect Cepheid or RR Lyrae variable stars. Beyond those galaxies methods are used that involve even more assumptions than those associated with Cepheid and RR Lyrae stars, such as the magnitudes of supergiant stars, or the distances that would make the observed angular dimensions of the HII regions correspond with the linear dimensions we assume for those objects in the Milky Way. At still greater distances, it is assumed that the brightest member in a cluster of galaxies has the same absolute magnitude as all other brightest members of other clusters. The methods that are used grow less and less precise for objects farther and farther from the sun. Here radiation is observed that was emitted in the ultraviolet, even though it is now redshifted into the visible, and not much is known about ultraviolet spectra of galaxies. There may be systematic errors in assessing their distances.

If it is accepted that the spectra of quasars are redshifted by tremendous amounts as observations seem to indicate and we apply Hubble's law, the quasars are the farthest objects in the universe. There seems no way of checking Hubble'a law independently. If the quasars were found not to satisfy Hubble's law, then tremendous doubt would be cast on all distances derived by Hubble's law, for one would never know whether we were observing an object that satisfied the law or not.

Some astronomers say that it would be too difficult for quasars to generate the amount of energy that is necesssary to make them as bright as they would need to be if they were very far from us. They feel that this problem of providing enough energy is so serious that they conclude that quasars must be "close" to us. This view is unattractive to many astronomers because it challenges Hubble's law and thus casts doubt on the present distance scale of the universe.

The principal attack on the theory that quasars are at great distances as indicated by their red shifts has come from Halton Arp of the Hale Observatories. He has been making observations of "peculiar galaxies," objects in the sky whose shapes deviate from the regularity of the shape of ordinary galaxies. These observations have led him to think that quasars might be linked to galaxies, both the peculiar and the ordinary types. He contends that he has found many examples in which two quasars are located on opposite sides of a galaxy from each other. He argues that the quasars and the galaxy must therefore be linked. The distances of the galaxies are determined from Hubble's law; if the quasars and galaxies are physically linked, then the quasars are at the same distance as the galaxies. These distances are much smaller than the quasar's red shifts indicate. A similar argument that Doppler distances cannot be trusted is made with Stephan's Quintet, five apparently linked galaxies, one of which has a red shift very different from the others. There are many astronomers, however, who criticize Arp's conclusions.

Further, even if one were to assume the correctness of the Hubble law, what is the value of H_o? Estimates of H_o have decreased from $H_o = 560$ km/$_{s/mpsc}$ in 1931 to present values in the range $50 < H_o < 110$ km/$_{s/mpsc}$ where 1 mp5c $= 3.25 \times 10^6$ light-years. Also, what is the concrete evidence to support the assumption that H_o is a universal constant? Why must it be a constant independent of place and direction? How does one know that expansion is linear and isotropic? The density of the matter and energy is not constant in our neighborhood so how can H_o be a constant?

Finally, de Vaucouleurs[8] claims that the relation $v = H_o r$ is not correct, but should be of the form $v = H_o r^2$ at small distances (out to the Virgo Cluster).

If Hubble's law is correct (and it appears that should be a strong if), it would appear to be nothing more than a kinematical expression. Allen's paper shows that there are infinitely many simple and noncontrived initial cosmic states, all of which lead to a universe that is expanding under the Hubble's law. Hubble expansion tells one virtually nothing about initial cosmic states. It certainly does not imply the singular initial state (a superpositioned universe). There is no need to postulate a big bang in order to counter- act the overwhelming gravitational field that would accompany such a singularly dense initial state. Allen argues that if astronomers had found galaxies to be moving in a "random" way, just as if they were the molecules of a gas, most people would recognize that the present cosmic state tells one nothing about an initial cosmic state. Further, most people would recognize the present cosmic state as a "natural" state that need not be ex- plained with some singular event, such as the big bang. Allen shows that, in spite of the apparent orderliness of the universe as actually observed, the expansion of the universe under the Hubble's law is a strictly random state. No more should be read into this big- bang expansion than should be read into the random motion of the molecules in a cloud of gas.

Allen refers to recent computer simulations that indicate that a system of n gravitating masses breaks up, even when the total energy is negative. As a result, almost any initial phase-space distribution results in a universe that eventually expands according to Hubble's law. Especially it does not imply the singularly dense superpositional state used in the big-bang model.

2. There is no evidence that galaxies are slowing down in their headlong flight, nor that they have done so in the past, as they surely should because of mutual gravitation between the galaxies. Also, the laws established by the Creator, believed to be univer- sally applicable, would have to be severely bent in order to allow for a static (motionless) universe. Both of these problems could possibly be reconciled with observations if we

abrogate the evidence of the Doppler effect and substitute some other cause of the red shift.   On the other hand, an original big bang could have propelled the matter initially at such speeds that the escape velocity dictated by the quantity of mass was exceeded. But even so, some slowing down should have taken place before the entities got out of gravitational range from each other, and there ought to be some evidence for it.   This all assumes that somehow elementary particles of matter and radiation moving from the explosion at terrifically high speeds "became" stars and galaxies.

3.   From the big-bang hypothesis it is predicted that all galaxies should be the same age.   However, from the determiners of age established by the evolutionists, galaxies are of all different ages.   This great variety of galaxies is not surprising at all from the Creation.

Although the evolutionist tries to explain the properties of the main type of galaxy in the Hubble sequence of galaxies in terms of objects all of the same age forming stars at different rates, there is no real evidence for this.   If star formation in elliptical galaxies proceeded at the same rate as in the Milky Way, they would have to be about ten times older than the Milky Way to have so little gas left?   This leads to an inconsistency in the big-bang scheme of things.   The evolutionist ideas are one big set of inconsistencies.

4.   Lemaitre, who originally suggested the big-bang hypothesis, said that the universe started out in a highly contracted state and initially expanded at a rapid rate. The expansion slowed down and came to a halt in a state similar to the Einstein universe (a static model), zero expansion.   Galaxies formed at this stage and gave rise to a new expanding phase that continued indefinitely.   The difficulty here is that the universe is supposed to be all there is (or self-contained), but allegedly starts moving again after

stopping, which is seemingly impossible since, according to Newton's first law of motion, an object will continue in whatever state of motion it is in, unless acted upon by an unbalanced external force so, if it were sitting still it would have to remain like that (in other words, no further expansion).   But in Lemaitre's universe the expansion just picked up again after galaxies, clusters of galaxies, etc. formed.

Further, galaxies are thought to have condensed out of an initially uniform gas. If this gas were in rapid expansion, moving radially from the region of the big bang, how was it possible to counteract the expansion in order to force the gas to contract into galaxies and stars and clusters of these objects?   As Lifshitz[9] pointed out, the rapid expansion would make it impossible to form nuclei of condensation to form these highly complex systems by gravitational collapse.   Further, how does rotation of galaxies originate from a big bang since the momentum is radial, not angular?

5.   According to George Gamow, at the end of 30 minutes after the big bang slightly more than half of the primordial material was converted into hydrogen, slightly less than half into helium.   However, in getting past helium some difficulty is encountered. A gap exists at atomic mass 5 among nuclides that can actually be formed, since neither a proton nor a neutron can be attached to a helium nucleus of atomic mass 4.   There seems no way around this difficulty.

6.   The Second Law of Thermodynamics argues that as a result of the explosion the entropy would increase and there should be no ordered systems formed.   It is inconceivable to this writer how an explosion could give rise to ordered arrangements such as stars and galaxies since in all common experience explosions produce disorder.   The present state of the universe is exceedingly complex, and hence requires a large quantity of information for its specification.   But the Second Law of Thermodynamics states that

the information contained in a macroscopic description of an isolated physical system in a simple state can never increase. If the initial state of the universe is assumed simple and the present complex, this would be contradicted by the fact that in the course of the expansion an irreversible generation of entropy (loss of information) must occur.

To repeat, the big-bang model assumes that the universe started from the expansion of an initially highly concentrated volume of energy and matter. Shortly after the explosion the elements are synthesized (though now most of the elements are considered to be formed in the interiors of stars) and there is formed a homogeneous, expanding spherical cloud of atoms, elementary particles, and photons which over 10 to 20 billion years evolves into the present real universe. Let's examine this a little from the thermodynamic viewpoint.

The homogeneous cloud expands irreversibly into a vacuum. This is similar to an ideal gas expanding irreversibly and adiabatically into a vacuum. Obviously, radiation expanding into a vacuum would cause an increase in entropy. The explosion is an entropy-producing process.

The evolutionist says the universe is an isolated system. The Second Law of Thermodynamics applies to such systems. Here then, is an ideal case for a thermodynamic investigation of a system. We will follow R. E. Kofahl's very excellent paper, A CRITIQUE OF THE MONOBLOC ARGUMENT OF R. M. THORNTON (private communication).

The entropy of such a bounded system can be expressed by the Boltzman phrasing of the Second Law of Thermodynamics: $S = k \ln \Omega$ where Ω is taken to be the number of quantum states available to the system when it is in any given macroscopic energy state. With the expanding cloud of the big bang Ω would be increasing and, thus, S would have to increase. Then no ordered systems could arise.

The present universe is highly differentiated. Over the observable universe we find great temperature gradients and differences, highly different concentrations of matter in highly differentiated chemical compositions and physical states, and undergoing a myriad of different processes involving mechanical, chemical, electromagnetic, and gravitational interactions. A common quantity observable in the real universe is the angular momentum of planets, stars, galaxies, dust and gas clouds, clusters, etc. - a highly ordered energy state. Astronomers postulate vast galactic synchotrons whirling streams of electrons through immense magnetic fields - highly ordered systems.

The real universe represents a vastly smaller number of available quantum states (Ω) than does the nature-myth called the big bang which has been described. How could all the gradients, differentiations, energy transforming process, ordered bodies, etc. come about in a big bang (an entropy-producing process) without a violation of the entropy law (a decrease in entropy)?

If, as the relativists propose, space is actually expanding with the outer envelope of the cloud, is there any useful order in the system? The cloud then occupies all the space that exists. The only order that the system would possess would be the velocity of the radiation and particles in a radial direction. The only thing happening would be that new space is becoming occupied with matter and radiation and the cloud is becoming less dense.

Some have proposed that vast eddies developed in the expanding cloud resulting in the real universe. But what caused the rotating eddies since the cloud is supposedly homogeneous, uniform, and possessing only radial momentum? Such a fantasy to credit unexplained eddies in a homogeneous system with creation of the real universe. There is no really credible explanation of the required processes to produce this highly structured universe when the analysis is based on a solid, comprehensive application of known physical laws.

7.   As previously mentioned, the cosmic expansion makes condensation of matter very difficult if only gravitational self-attraction is considered.   A difficulty in the case of the expanding universe is that no large-scale condensations initially exist to provide condensation nuclei around which galaxies could form.   The gathering of enough matter to form a galaxy or a star or a cluster of these objects seems nearly impossible in any of the expanding universe cosmologies.   It seems that none of the conditions can be met by the expanding universe cosmologies in order for galaxies and related objects to form at all.

8.   If the galaxies, presently seen to be expanding into space, were together in one small region of space some time in the past, did that time mark the beginning of the universe?   According to the big-bang hypothesis (at least Lemaitre's and Gamow's version of it) before this time there were no galaxies, just a great superdense cloud of gas, a cosmic egg, you might say.   Something caused the cloud to expand violently and rush outwards in all directions.   The expanding gas somehow broke up into individual clouds that became clusters of galaxies.   Within each cluster galaxy-cloud still smaller clouds gave birth to galaxies and star clusters and individual stars.   And as some of the individual stars formed, "leftover" gas and dust packed itself into planets.   However, some of the gas and dust never formed stars, and remained as free matter thinly spread out in space among the stars. The very pertinent question that arises immediately is: If this universe is "all there is," what could have caused a "cosmic egg" sitting in equilibrium, presumably for an eternity to begin to expand violently of its own accord, since this would be a violation of Newton's first law of motion which claims that it takes an external force to

change the state of an object sitting in equilibrium? If something inside the system disturbed it, it could not have been in equilibrium.

9. Further, this primeval atom or cloud was, according to Lemaitre, of radius about that of the solar system, or according to Gamow, infinitely big. Regardless of its exact size, it is cause for wonder how an explosion could be propagated over an effectively infinite distance in either of the models.

10. Again, if the motion of the elementary particles and the radiation were radically outward from the explosion and was also uniform in composition, density, etc. where did the rotational motion of star, galaxies, clusters, etc. originate since all the initial momentum was radial and not angular momentum.

IV. THE STEADY-STATE OR CONTINUOUS CREATION COSMOGONIC HYPOTHESIS

A. THE STEADY-STATE HYPOTHESIS

The notion that the universe had a finite beginning in time and progresses in such a way as to lead to a heat death eventually is philosophically unacceptable to many astronomers. Several astronomers with this view, including Herman Bondi, Thomas Gold and Fred Hoyle, introduced the perfect cosmological principle, as already discussed, to get around this situation. Their cosmological model extended the principle of isotropy, already referred to, so that not only does the universe appear the same from any vantage point, it appears the same at all times--past, present and future. The motion of the expansion of the universe is retained, but as galaxies move apart, matter is spontaneously created to fill the void (hence the name: continuous creation cosmogonic hypothesis); from the new matter, presumably new galaxies are formed. Thus, the process of creation is continuous; the universe is very large and infinitely old, though showing no signs of old age. There was no beginning and there will be no end. The "creation" of matter is supposed to proceed at a rate of one atom per cubic meter of space in every 3×10^5 years.

Those who originally proposed the steady-state theory maintained that there was a continuous "creation of hydrogen atoms out of nothing" and without a Creator. In place of a world of nebulae proceeding as a whole through an irreversible change, they proposed a universe finite in space but remaining, as a whole, forever the same.

To the knowledge of this writer there is not a shred of evidence for the steady-state hypothesis. The idea of the continual creation of matter has not emerged from mathematical discussion based on scientific observation. It has no other basis than the fancy of a few mathematicians who think how nice it would be if the world were made that way. The mathematics follows the fancy, not precedes it; the fancy is credited because it gives scope for mathematical exercise, not because there is any reason to believe it true.

B. ARGUMENTS AGAINST THE STEADY-STATE THEORY

1. Granting for the sake of argument that the nebular red shift indicates that nebulae are continually receding into inaccessibility by surpassing the speed of light, the steady-state advocates are asking us to believe that isolated fundamental particles are continually created within the accessible region in order to maintain the same total quantity of observable matter at all times. For a nebula, on reaching the speed of light, is still observable from another nebula not so far distant in the same direction, and the process would have been observable there before becoming knowable to us. Hence, the sudden vanishing of nebulae moving at relatively slow speeds should be observable from one nebula and, therefore from all. This situation then would constitute a violation of the first cosmological principle. It would seem that the recession of nebulae into unob-

servability and the creation of particles close at hand would be independent processes. Yet, according to the steady-state scheme of things, they occur at the same rate--not approximately, but exactly, for the universe must appear the same eternally--eternally in the past and eternally in the future. This certainly seems a pre-established harmony to put it mildly.

2. In the steady-state cosmology the followers are predisposed to assert the equivalence of events at all places and at all times in the universe, but the evidence is all against this. Every process we know, on the small or large scale, is a one-way process, showing a preference for one direction over the opposite. The system of nebulae expands and does not contract, gravitation is an attraction and not a repulsion, the entropy of a closed system increases and does not decrease, every chemical process tends toward a state of equilibrium from which the substances concerned do not themselves depart, and so on. There is nothing in nature that indicates that any course of events is reversible.

3. According to the founders of this nature-myth, Thomas Gold, Fred Hoyle and Herman Bondi, the creation of one hydrogen atom per year in a volume of space equal to that of the Empire State Building is enough to keep the universe in a steady state. So we must picture a universe in which the density of matter remains constant while the volume increases. But where do the new hydrogen atoms required to keep density constant come from? Where does the infinite supply of hydrogen for new galaxy formation come from?

According to Gold, they create themselves out of nothing. As Bondi and Gold emphasize the creation of hydrogen atoms is a creation ex nihilo. This is a self-contradictory concept, creatio ex nihilo, without a Creator. Bondi in his book, COSMOLOGY, on page 144 states, "It should be understood that creation discussed is the formation of matter not out of radiation but out of nothing."

Later on there was introduced the idea of a "creation field." This was done by an extension of Einstein's equations of the four-dimensional space-time continuum. The "C-field," as it is called, is said to propagate through space much as a magnetic or gravitational field, but is effective at greater distances than any of the recognized types of fields.

As in the case of known fields, the C-field results from the presence of matter. If there are several contributions to the strength of the C-field in any given region, their effect is additive and can build up the intensity of the point where "matter happens." A particle forms if the C-field carries at least as much energy as the rest mass of the particle.

Hoyle figures that there is energy to spare. Baryons such as neutrons can be created with high initial velocities, in a mode similar to the process of pair-production in which electrons and positrons are formed from gamma rays. The created matter is capable of generating a C-field of its own which can participate in the formation of more matter.

This whole concept is a violation of the First Law of Thermodynamics. This law says that the total amount of energy and the total amount of matter in the universe is a constant. It would forbid the creation of energy out of nothing.

Further, this mythical rate of "creation" when submitted to direct test by monitoring devices carried through outer space by artificial satellites certainly have found no trace of the alleged "creation."

4. Any matter created in an already existing galaxy would be trapped there. The galaxy would get more and more massive while still having nuclear fuel to burn to make it visible. So we should be able to see unbelievably enormous galaxies so far as their masses are concerned. This is not the case at all.

5. The radio-frequency radiation of $3°K$ coming to us from all directions cannot be explained by the steady-state hypothesis. ✓

6. In 1960 at Mt. Palomar quasi-stellar radio objects or quasars were discovered. The quasars emitted strong radio radiation, but unlike the majority of radio sources, they appeared star-like on photographic plates. Their spectra exhibited a puzzling pattern of emission lines. These spectral features were deciphered as enormously red-shifted lines normally found in the far ultraviolet spectra. Interpreted as Doppler shifts, the displaced spectral lines indicated velocities approaching the speed light; assuming they fit the so-called Hubble law relating distance and red shift, then their distances have to be immense. From this it followed that their luminosities must be incredibly large in order to be seen so well at such great distances. The steady-state hypothesis could not explain this lack of homo-geneity in space posed by the existence of the quasars.

7. Obviously, the Second Law of Thermodynamics contradicts the steady-state hypothesis since the universe must be running down toward a state of maximum disorder. This would argue that the universe is finite in time so far as its age is concerned.

Further, it was far more complicated at its beginning than it is now. This negates the ideas of the steady-state hypothesis.

V. INDICATORS OF THE AGE OF THE UNIVERSE

A. INTRODUCTION

The age of the universe has been the object of intense study and wide speculation. There are certain fundamental unknowns in the problem that seem impossible of determination but definite upper limits may be assessed on the age of the universe. The inability of scientists to describe the origin of things, the explaining of all things in an evolutionary framework, and the feeling that the uniformitarian geologist is right about the age of the earth has led astronomers to push the age of the universe further and further back in time, hiding all the unsolvable problems of the naturalistic cosmogonies behind a veil of time.   The beginning of the universe, if one follows the "big-bang" model, would be at 10 to 20 billion years ago.   If one believes the "continuous-creation" model, though it is in rather ill repute today, he would say the universe is infinitely old, having no real beginning and, supposedly, no end.   The opposing position to these naturalistic views is that the universe was created a short time ago with all the celestial bodies that make up the universe coming into existence simultaneously.   This position maintains that there is a Creator, which is basic and original, "which exists on its own."   This Creator has caused all the other things (the universe) and this universe will cease to exist if the Creator ceases to maintain it.   The very long time scale is extremely important in the naturalistic nature-myths since a young universe would be the "death" of the big-bang and steady-state concepts.

The age of the universe is hard to come by, but it is very easy to approach the problem with ready-made answers.   However, it is possible to pick up some clues which will tell us whether it is young or old.   If the universe is very old (on the order of billions of years), it should show certain signs of age.   Let's assume for this discussion the "big-bang" model of the origin of the universe, since this version holds the center stage of cosmogony today.   From this model we should expect the universe to show its age by certain appearances. Let's see if this old age for the stellar system is really the case, or if a youthfulness is more the appearance of the stars, galaxies, clusters of galaxies, and dust and gas in space.   This monograph will have listed in it only a few of the many time indices for the age of the universe since this is the subject of another monograph presently in preparation.

B.   AN AGE INDEX FOR THE BIG-BANG MODEL

The "big-bang" concept starts with all the matter in the universe concentrated in a superdense core with a density of 10^{25} g/cm^3 and a temperature in excess of 10^{16} K^o. The alleged initial superdense, hot cosmic fluid was a mix of the strongly interacting elementary particles composed of mesons, protons, neutrons, etc., and a smaller proportion of photons and the lighter-weight muons, electrons, neutrinos, etc. Supposedly there was anti-matter present also.   At the near instantaneous origin of time by this scheme, there was the annihilation of heavier elementary particles into gamma radiation resulting in a huge fireball.   Then the lightweight particles annihilated each other, continuing the tremendous fireball. The fireball stage ends as radiation decouples from matter. Quasars and clusters of proto-galaxies condense.   And, finally, galaxies and stars form and, it is said, they are still forming today. There you have it--"the big bang"--tremendously exciting but not a shred of evidence to prove it and much to disprove the notion in the first place!

Using the conventional model of star formation based on the above described "big bang," as matter expanded outward from the explosion, stars were formed by gravitational collapse of huge, turbulent clouds of hydrogen. The cloud temperature was raised as gravitational potential energy was given up when the cloud presumably collapsed. At some stage thermonuclear reactions became possible because of the high temperatures ($\approx 10^6$'s ^{o}K) supposedly generated in the cloud, and hydrogen was converted to energy and helium according to processes involving the proton-proton cycle, the C-N-O cycle, etc. With the passage of time the various heavier chemical elements should be formed in the stars.   As time elapses the chemical composition of the stars and, of course, the interstellar medium (material between the stars) should change considerably, says this model. After 15 to 20 billion years there should be rather tremendous chemical evolution of the universe. This, then, is one of the signs of aging for the universe in this big-bang concept. What do we see?

The spectra of a wide variety of stars show atmospheric compositions for them very similar to that of the sun. The similarity in abundance for stars of as widely differing "ages" as a Bo star, which, according to the evolutionary scheme, formed only a few million years ago, and a red giant or the planetary nebulae, which by the evolutionary scheme, should be among the oldest objects in the galaxy and, hence, seven or more billion years old, indicate that the interstellar medium has hardly changed at all. There is this serious lack of evidence for so-called chemical evolution. In other words, the Sun, a very "young" Bo star, Tau Scorpii, planetary nebulae, a red giant ϵ Virginis, and many other "normal" stars all have the same chemical composition, within the limits of observational error. This is significant because the alleged ages of these objects cover the whole supposed lifetime of the Milky Way.

These analyses show that throughout this supposed lifetime of the galaxy the interstellar matter has had an almost unchanged composition. There are a small number of exceptional stars, however, that do show a quite different chemical make-up than the other stellar bodies. But the stars that are suspected of being the oldest show abundances of the elements from carbon to barium that are two magnitudes smaller than the "younger" stars like the sun when they should be much larger. This evidence would seem to indicate that the universe is nothing near its alleged age since it shows practically no change, or that the energy generation processes in the stars and their exchange with the interstellar medium are not remotely understood, or both!

C.   AGE OF GALAXIES

The formation of galaxies in the first place seems to be an insurmountable difficulty for all the various naturalistic cosmogonies.   There are some observations that would lead

one to believe that galaxies are of recent origin and,thus, do not fit the time scheme of

the naturalistic cosmogonies:

1.   Galaxies never appear to occur singly. They are only found in pairs or in

larger aggregates.

2.   In general, the masses of the galaxies that are members of a physically

well isolated group or cluster seem to be smaller than the mass that would be required to

bind the galaxies gravitationally. Thus, the groups or clusters of galaxies must be of

recent origin or they would have long ago disintegrated the groupings by their tremendous

velocities exceeding the escape speeds for the clusters.

3.   Some pairs of or multiple galaxies are joined by bridges of luminous matter.

In a few cases it has been noted that the speeds of the galaxies along the radial direc-

tion alone are of the order of several thousand kilometers per second so that these

galaxies cannot be gravitationally bound and would separate quite rapidly.   They,

therefore, must have originated recently, and it would seem as completely formed galaxies!

4.   Further, a galaxy is an assemblage of stars that cannot rotate as a rigid body;

the inner parts revolve in shorter times than the outer. An enormous difficulty which all

theories that propose a large age for the universe encounter is that any spiral-arm structure

will be wound up into a near circle in one to a few (at most) revolutions of the galaxy--

200 million to 500 million years.   The magnetic field which runs through the gases in a

spiral arm is not strong enouch to give the arm appreciable rigidity, and further, the stars

in the arms are not coupled to this magnetic field.   In other words, the galaxy will wrap

itself up in a, relatively speaking, short time.   This analysis does not, of course, determine the

age of the universe, but certainly seems to put an upper limit on its age.   This limit is far

smaller than the time called for by the evolutionist astronomer.

D. TIME SCALE FOR GENERATION
OF STELLAR ENERGY

Another problem regarding the ages of the stars comes from the Eddington mass-luminosity law that has to do with the rate at which stars burn up their energy. Very massive stars burn up their energy so much faster than less massive stars that they cannot last nearly as long. The Eddington mass-luminosity law says that the power radiated by a star is given by the expression: $L = k M^{3.4}$. It is argued that the very bright and hot stars (O and B) must be of recent origin since, if they were born at the alleged beginning of things with their present very large masses, they should have burned out long ago.

It used to be thought that all the stars were the same age. There is the co-existence of giant (20 x Sun's mass) and dwarfs (1 x Sun's mass) in the same clusters. If they had the same origin from the same source, how could they differ in age?   If we imagine time to run backward from the present instant, it is found by R. A. Lyttleton that a star's mass will build up to infinity in a small fraction of the time that it would take for the hydrogen content of the star to diminish by one-half with time running the ordinary way.

If an old age for the galaxy and the manner of evolution of a star advocated by most astronomers (though no one has seen a star go through a lifetime), is assumed, it is somewhat marginal whether the galaxy is old enough for a one-solar mass star to have evolved to the white dwarf stage, but it certainly is not old enough for a star of one-half solar mass to have done so.   Yet white dwarfs with masses this small are known. How then can the age estimates be correct at all?   It would seem that the universe was created with stars of all forms and appearances and in various groupings with different motions.

Some of the "oldest" galactic clusters appear to have little compositional differ-ences from the youngest ones, even though they supposedly approach the alleged age of the globular clusters which in the evolutionary scheme are supposed to be very old.   I think

this is a further clue arguing for a recent origin.

E.   TIME FOR BREAK UP OF STAR CLUSTERS

There are groupings of stars much smaller than the galaxies called clusters.

These clusters are of different types according to their shape, constituents, and distri-

bution in the galaxy.   These star clusters are breaking up due to high speeds of the com-

ponent stars that overcome the self-gravitation of the cluster.   The stars are presumably

diverging from a common point so fast that, in some cases, if their motions were projected

backwards to this common point the cluster could have originated only several thousand

years ago.   Most astronomers believe that the stars and the cluster of which they are a

member came into existence at roughly the same time.   We have many star clusters that

are disintegrating so rapidly that their ages can in no way be on the order of a billion or

billions of years.   There is no evidence for the formation of stars taking place now.   This

seems to argue strongly for a young age of the stars and clusters.

F.   TIME AND THE "MISSING" MASS
OF CLUSTERS OF GALAXIES

Galaxies and clusters of galaxies are objects of much concerted study today.

Galaxies in clusters are bound together by gravitational forces and, thus, provide a sort

of laboratory for observation of interactions of incredible amounts of matter and energy.

Galaxies never appear to occur singly, as already remarked, but in clusters.   They are

found in pairs or in larger aggregates.   Some pairs or multiple galaxies are joined by

bridges of luminous matter.   In a few cases the velocities of the galaxies along

the radial direction alone are of the order of many thousand kilometers per second so that it is not likely that these galaxies are gravitationally bound. They would, therefore,

seem to have originated quite recently.   In general, the mass of galaxies that are members

of a physically well isolated group or cluster seem to be smaller than the mass that would be

required to bind the galaxies gravitationally.

A galaxy is a collection of some hundred billion stars held together by gravity.

Our galaxy, the Milky Way, is a member of a cluster consiting of about twenty galaxies

in all, called the Local Group. The Local Group is a very small cluster compared to most

of the hundreds of clusters thus far observed and catalogued.   An average cluster has one

or two hundred members, while the largest contains several thousand galaxies.

The nearest cluster outside of the Local Group is thought to be about 500 billion

kilometers away in Euclidean measurement.   The most distant known clusters lie around 200

times farther away, at the very edge of the observable universe. The distances are ob-

tained by rather indirect methods based on assumptions difficult to prove.   This should

always be kept in mind when distances of astronomical objects are given. Two of the richest

clusters, one in the direction of the constellation Virgo and one in Coma Berenices, are at

relatively small distances and have been studied carefully.

For the galaxies studied in the Coma Cluster, the average velocity of recession is

about 7000 kilometers per second. This is determined from studies of the red shifts of the

light from these galaxies, which is considered to indicate a radial motion toward or away

from the observer, assuming the red shift of the starlight is an actual Doppler effect.

Each individual galaxy ordinarily has some smaller, random motion inside the cluster.

This speed is around several hundred kilometers per second with reference to the neighboring

galaxies in the cluster.   Thus, the members should eventually escape from the Coma Cluster and wander off into intercluster space if there is not enough force to keep them in the cluster. If the universe is at least 4.5 billion years old, the random motions of the galaxies should have long ago disrupted the cluster and the galaxies could not possibly be as close together as they are now. As a matter of fact, there should be no clusters at all. The force that would counteract this escape tendency is the gravitational force of the mass of the cluster on the galaxy. The gravitational force of the matter in the earth pulls back a baseball thrown from its surface; though if projected hard enough the baseball will escape from the earth. In the Coma Cluster, the random motions of the galaxies would have to be balanced by the gravitational attraction of the matter in the cluster if the cluster is to stay together. This random motion of the galaxies in the cluster is called the velocity dispersion.

The velocity dispersion of the cluster can be calculated from the measured red shifts of the galaxies. The mass of a galaxy is related to its brightness. When the total mass of all the galaxies in the cluster is determined, the gravitational force can be calculated and compared with the observed velocity dispersion. The result has surprised and astonished astronomers no end. In the Coma Cluster the mass is too little to counterbalance the velocity dispersion, by a factor of seven. In other words, for every seven kilograms of mass necessary to hold the cluster together, only one kilogram can be accounted for. This is not a trivial matter. There is only fourteen percent of the matter in the cluster that should be there in order for the cluster to stay together. Astronomers have looked high and low for this "missing mass," but it is nowhere to be found. Things get worse in this search when other clusters than the Coma Cluster are studied; from two to ten times the needed mass is missing.

Some have thought that the "missing mass" is located in intergalactic space.

To be detected, the matter would have to emit some form of electromagnetic radiation such as x-rays, visible light, or radio waves. The background x-radiation that is incident on the earth's atmosphere can be explained by other means than the presence of a diffuse intergalactic material permeating space and emitting x-rays. If cold matter exists between the galaxies, radio waves might be emitted and the radio astronomer could detect this. However, this has not been observed, and if small quantities of cold matter did escape detection they would be far too small in an amount to keep the clusters together. A hot gas would emit x-rays. Certainly x-radiation has been observed associated with some galaxies. But the presence of the radiation has been explained rather well in terms not involving an intergalactic medium. A slightly warm material would be hard to detect since the radiation would be in the ultraviolet range of wavelengths, which are mainly strained out by our atmosphere. However, using detection equipment in high-altitude rockets, balloons, and satellites there has been no indication of a slightly warm gas between the galaxies. The "missing mass" is not in the form of a diffuse gas in inter-galactic space.

Further conditions have been placed on this "missing mass." A study of the dynamics of the dispersion of the galaxies would indicate that the matter cannot be postu-lated as existing in one very massive object that does not have luminosity. The matter has to be distributed as a common constituent of intergalactic space. If someone says that alleged "black holes" (which, if they exist at all, would have such a tremendously large gravitational pull that light cannot escape from their surfaces and, thus, they would be invisible) account for this matter, they would have to suppose these "black holes" to be as commonly located as galaxies. As Margon[12] points out, there would have to be hundreds of thousands of them. There is no evidence for this situation. Again Margon[11] says the same objection applies to "dead" galaxies (non-luminous) or the large number of cool stars.

The obvious conclusion seems to be that the "missing mass" is not really missing since it apparently wasn't there to start with. The universe then could be quite young, and other lines of evidence strongly indicate this. The break-up time for these clusters (the time for dispersion of the galaxies so that there are no clusters) is far, far less than the alleged evolutionary age of the universe. This means that the clusters, since they have not been destroyed, are young, as well as the galaxies that form them. These galaxies contain stars that are alleged by the evolutionists to be the oldest objects in the universe (ten to twenty billion years old in the evolutionary scheme of things). This rapid break-up of the clusters coupled with the fact that, nonetheless, clusters still exist in the universe would indicate that these allegedly old stars are not old at all. The Coma Cluster could not be younger than the Milky Way. So if the cluster is young, the galaxy is young and the objects within the galaxy are young. The break-up times of clusters are on the order of just a few millions of years at the very most. So the present existence of clusters argues that the universe has not reached anywhere near that age, even much less the age demanded by the evolutionists.

Also, it has been noted that the motions of the clusters look like those of bound systems which are not breaking up. If that is so, then the clusters would certainly be young, not having reached a stage where they are showing a looseness of organization indicative of much age.

To avoid the obvious conclusion regarding time which strikes at the heart of evolutionary hypothesis astronomers go to great lengths in inventing explanations regarding the "missing mass." Margon[12] suggests that "we have reached an impasse, almost to the point Thomas Kuhn has called a scientific revolution." Apparently, unless the experimental data are blatantly in error, it is inevitable that some cherished astronomical or physical principle must fall. It would seem that the axe should fall upon the supposed aeons-long age that is assigned _a priori_ to the universe, the solar system, and the earth, for this concept of huge quantities of time leads to contradictory and illogical positions in many aspects of astrophysics.

G. THE VARIABLE "CONSTANTS" OF RADIOMETRIC "CLOCKS"

Since the data from radiometric "clocks" are sometimes cited as establishing the time-scale for stellar evolution and cosmogony it would be of value to consider some recent developments in this area. Radioactivity was discovered in the late 1800's. It was stated early that no external effects could change the disintegration constants of radio-active elements. Radioactive elements are those chemical elements that decay into daughter elements by emission or absorption of energy and particles in the nuclei of their atoms. On the basis of experimental evidence in those early years of study of these elements it was concluded that radioactive decay rates do not change, that these rates cannot be affected by external means, and that only the nuclei of the atoms of these radioactive elements were involved in the decay processes.

The geologists, of course, immediately seized upon these decay processes as constituting clocks to determine when geological events occurred and the age of the earth. If uranium decays into lead at a constant rate, and if a rock from some mountain contains uranium and lead, the age of the rock and the mountain, perhaps, may be found by simply calculating the time to obtain the lead by decay from the uranium. It is more involved, of course, but that is the essence of the method by which the radiometric "clocks" work.

Among a number of requirements for a radioactive element and its daughter product to constitute a "clock" for geological events is the necessity that the "clock" run without variation. Well, evolutionist geologists have long ignored the evidence of

variability in the radii of pleochroic haloes, which shows that the decay rates are not con-

stant and would, thus, deny that some radioactive elements such as uranium could be

clocks.[13] Emery[14] in a very important paper has shown that there is excellent laboratory

evidence that external influences can change the decay rates. He reported that fourteen

different radionuclides have had their decay properties changed by effects such as pressure,

temperature, electric and magnetic fields, stress in monomolecular layers, etc.

Dudley[15] has proposed, "Rather than assuming that radioactivity is a series of

(spontaneous) unrelated events occurring without prior cause, a theoretical approach was

developed which translates the 'neutrino sea' concept of astrophysics and cosmology to

nuclear physics. This postulates a radioactive atom to be a 'linear resonant system,

subject to parametric excitation.'" Thus, the decay constant used in the equations for

obtaining ages of geological events becomes a variable dependent on the energy state of

all the atom and not just the nucleus. Half-lives would not be constant. The decay

constant would instead be a stability index of the element.

If this is the case, as the evidence seems to indicate, then the forces and the

tremendous amounts of energy involved in some processes and happenings in the universe

could strongly alter the "decay" rates. The alleged radiometric "clocks" are then not

really usable as age determiners at all for the earth and thus for the solar system and

the stellar universe, actually they mainly have been used as window-dressing by the geolo-

gists since the preconceived views of theoretical historical geology based on the evolutionary

persuasion set the ages of earth history even before radioactivity was discovered.

H. HOW LONG TO FORM AN INTERSTELLAR GRAIN?

The space between the stars is composed of atoms, molecules and grains of matter. The stars allegedly formed by gravitational collapse from clouds of this material. It is rather baffling how an interstellar grain of matter forms since the density of matter in interstellar space is so low.

Consider the growth rate of a grain which starts with some radius that, of course, will change with time. If this grain forms in space by the sticking of interstellar atoms and molecules to this nucleus grain as they impinge on it at some speed, the growth rate can be roughly calculated. Using the most favorable conditions and the maximum possible sticking ability for grains, Harwit[16] has determined a growth rate of 10^{-22} centimeters per second (or one-ten-thousand-billion-billionth centimeter per second). To reach a size of just a hundred-thousandth of a centimeter in radius under these most favorable conditions it would take about three billion years. Using more likely values for sticking ability of particles, it would take a time interval greater than the alleged evolutionary age of the galaxy--more than twenty billion years. Of course, this supposes the grain will form in the first place. This seems impossible though since the hydrogen that would be deposited on the grain would ordinarily evaporate right back off very rapidly. Sputtering by fast moving protons can easily jar loose the atoms on the surface of the grain even after they become attached. The formation of molecules poses just as great a difficulty as the formation of dust grains. It is easy to destroy them but very difficult, if not impossible, to form them on the basis of known physical processes in interstellar space.

If it takes as long to form such a simple object as an interstellar grain as the calculations indicate under the most hopeful of conditions (that do not actually exist at all), how can the notion of huge ages for the stars and galaxies have any credibility and be taken seriously? Effects such as evaporation, sputtering, and vapor pressure would seem to destroy any grains that might have formed.

I. CONCLUSIONS ABOUT TIME

These clues do not exactly determine the actual age of the universe but do put upper limits on the age. These upper limits deny the huge time span necessary for the evolutionist's case. The signs say the universe is young.

The myth that unlimited time is available in which the evolutionists may frame their schemes to explain things has been around for quite a while now. However, the scientific evidence continues to accumulate labelling the huge ages of the universe, the solar system, and the earth as a fable, not a conclusion reached by an adherence to scientific proof.

VI. <u>CONCLUSIONS</u>

Was there really a big bang? I believe that the answer clearly must be no! When we come to the universe in total and the large number of complex objects in it, the big bang is able to explain nothing. Further, the age of the universe appears to be young, not old as is demanded by the big bang and steady-state hypotheses.

To repeat (in order to emphasize the incredibility of the big bang as an explanation), the big bang supposedly is chaos leading to diversity and order. In other words, starting with an initial chaotic and homogeneous mixture of the three elements: radiation, hydrogen, and helium we are supposed to believe that this would end with, for example, our solar system, the earth, and life on it. The big-bang cosmology starts off with a very compact and heavy body comprising all energy and matter in the universe which disperses at very high speeds, and then, for reasons no one has been able to explain, some parts of the cloud stop expanding and condense to form the galaxies and these bodies within each galaxy, stars, and then as if by magic, start moving apart.

Disorganized, randomly oriented gas clouds are supposed eventually to produce highly organized compact bodies, such as complex stars and planets. Stars supposedly are recycled many times to account for the cosmic abundances of the elements since the big bang could not account for them. The preceding discussions have shown the futility of such fanciful speculations, but Professor F. M. Johnson's[17] little verse comes to mind as the big-bang hypothesis is considered:

> What power man has to believe
> With blindness or selective sieve;
> The universe must fit his mind
> Put facts and figures far behind.

Perhaps what Professor R. Benton[18] said regarding black holes could be applied to the followers of the big-bang cosmogony: "theoretical astrophysicists — some of the more renowned ones — are staring into a black box from which any number of assumptions can be made on the existence of things they envision from the nothingness they see." Truly we have suffered too long and too disastrously under serfdom to barren naturalistic nature-myths regarding the cosmology and the cosmogony of this actual universe. The evolutionist lives in a dream world in which any resemblance to the real world is lacking.

In the light of the data about our universe and the laws of physics and chemistry, the actual universe must be the result of intelligent design and intelligently ordered creation of space, matter, energy, time, motion and the initiation of intelligently ordered energy transformation by the infinite, omniscient, omnipotent Creator.

REFERENCES

1. Gamow, G. 1955. THE CREATION OF THE UNIVERSE, Viking, New York, p. 20.

2. Dingle, H. "Science and Modern Cosmology," Science, Vol. 120, October, 1954, p. 518.

3. de Vaucouleurs, G. "The Case for a Hierarchical Cosmology," Science, Vol. 167: 1203-1223.

4. Ibid, p. 1204.

5. Pecker, J. C., Roberts, A. P. and Vigier, J. P. "Non-Velocity Redshifts and Photon-Photon Interactions," Nature, Vol. 237, May 26, 1972, p. 227, 229.

6. Science News, Vol. 110, July 3, 1976, p. 6.

7. Allen, A. D. 1976. "The Big Bang Is Not Needed," Foundations of Physics, Vol. 6, No. 1, p. 59-63.

8. Rowan-Robinson, M. 1977. COSMOLOGY, Oxford University Press, p. 142.

9. Lifshitz, E. M. 1946. "On Gravitational Stability of the Expanding Universe," Journal of Physics, USSR, Vol. 10, p. 116.

10. Margon, B. 1975. "The Missing Mass," Mercury, January-February, p. 6.

11. Ibid, p. 6.

12. Ibid, p. 6.

13. Slusher, H. S. 1973. A CRITIQUE OF RADIOMETRIC DATING, Institute for Creation Research, San Diego.

14. Emery, G. T. 1972. "Perturbations of Nuclear Decay Rates," Annual Review Nuclear Science, Vol. 22.

15. Dudley, H. C., "Radioactivity Re-examined," Chemical and Engineering News, April 7, 1975, p. 2.

16. Harwit, M. 1973. ASTROPHYSICAL CONCEPTS, John Wiley & Sons, Inc., New York, p. 394.

REFERENCES

continued

17.   Johnson, F. M.   1977.   VOYAGE INTO ASTRONOMY, Kendall/Hunt
      Publishing Co., Dubuque, p. 267.

18.   Science News, Vol. 113, May 6, 1978, No. 18, p. 291.

DATE DUE

Hartzell			
NOV 13 81			
Hartell			
APR 03 1985			
APR 16 1985			
APR 20 1987			
MAY 5 1989			
APR 02 1991			
OCT 09 1995			
APR 01 2002			

JOSTEN'S 30 508